MEMORIAL SCHOOL

Ted and Sally

ARTHUR I. GATES
MIRIAM BLANTON HUBER
FRANK SEELY SALISBURY

THE MACMILLAN COMPANY : NEW YORK

Stories

The Wagon 5
  Ride in the Wagon 6
  Ride! Ride! 9
  Father and Mother 13
  Up the Hill 18
  Down We Go 22

The Play House 25
  A House To Play In . . . 26
  Sally and Ted 30
  Sally and Boots 33
  Sally and Tuffy 36
  The Dolls 39

Illustrated by
CHARLES PAYZANT AND ASSOCIATES
HELEN HANSEN, SYLVIA HOLLAND, JANET PAGE,
BASIL DAVIDOVICH, ERNEST TERRAZAS

© *The Macmillan Company 1951, 1957*
All Rights Reserved

PRINTED IN THE UNITED STATES OF AMERICA

9-D

Girls Play House 42

Boys Play Train 45

Ride in the Big Train . . . 48

The Dolls Ride 52

Here We Go to the Farm . 55

Come to the Farm 56

Boots and Tuffy 60

Here We Go 63

The Big Train 65

On the Train 71

We Eat on the Train . . . 73

To Bed on the Train . . . 78

Grandfather 81

Grandmother 85

Blue Hill Farm 87

Farm Boy and Farm Girl . . 88

Tuffy and the Red Hen . . . 90

Boots and the Ducks . . . 92

The Blue Boat 95

The Pet Pig 99
Find the Eggs 101
Pig! Pig! Pig! . . . 103
We Ride the Horses . . . 108
Father Is Coming . . . 112
The Farm Is Fun . . . 115
Going Home 120

**Funny Big Farm
and Funny Little Train** . 125

On the Funny Farm . . . 126
What Is It? 129
The Little Red Train . . 133
A Funny Ride . . . . .
Rainy Day at the Farm (Verse)
Marchette Chute 142

The Wagon

Ride in the Wagon

"Come, Boots," said Ted.
"Come and ride.
Come and ride in my wagon."

"Jump in, Boots," said Ted.
"Jump in and ride.
Ride in my wagon, Boots.
Jump in and ride."

7

"Here we go," said Ted.
"Here we go, Boots.
Ride in the wagon, Boots.
Ride, Boots, ride."

Ride! Ride!

"Look, Sally!" said Ted.
"See Boots ride.
See Boots ride in the wagon."

"Oh, Boots!" said Sally.
"I like to see you ride."

"Tuffy! Tuffy!" said Sally.
"Look at Boots ride.
I want you to ride.
Come, Tuffy.
Come and ride in the wagon."

"Get in, Sally," said Ted.
"Get in the wagon.
Get in the wagon with Tuffy.
He will ride with you."

"Here we go, Tuffy," said Sally.
"Run, Ted, run!"

"You get in, Ted," said Sally.
"You ride in the wagon.
Here, Boots!
Ride in the wagon with Ted.
Jump in, Boots."

"Here we go," said Ted.
"Ride! Ride! Ride!"

Father and Mother

"Here is Father," said Sally.
"He will ride in the wagon."

"Oh, Father!" said Ted.
"Come and ride.
Come and ride in the wagon."

13

"Look, Ted," said Sally.
"Here comes Mother.
Mother will ride.
Mother will ride in the wagon."

"No! No!" said Mother.
"I like to see you play.
You play with the wagon."

"Ride! Ride!" said Ted.
"Father, come and ride.
You will like it.
Mother, come and ride.
Come and ride in the wagon."

"No! No!" said Father.
"We are too big.
The wagon is too little.
We want to see you play.
You play with the wagon."

Sally said, "Come, Mother.
We want you to ride.
We want Father to ride."

"No! No!" said Mother.
"We are too big to ride."

"No! No!" said Father.
"The wagon is too little.
We are too big to ride."

Up the Hill

"Ted!" said Father.
"Go up the hill and ride down.
Ride down in the wagon."

"Oh, Sally!" said Mother.
"Go up the hill and ride down.
I want to see you ride down."

"Come, Tuffy," said Sally.
"Get in the wagon.
Ride up the hill in the wagon."

"Come, Boots," said Ted.
"Up the hill we go."

"Here we go," said Sally.
"Here we go up the hill."

Up the hill went Ted.
Up the hill went Sally, too.
Up the hill went the wagon.

"Here we are," said Ted.
"Get in the wagon, Sally.
Get in the wagon, Tuffy.
Get in and ride down the hill."

"Ted," said Sally.
"You get in the wagon, too.
You get in and ride."

"I will," said Ted.
"I will ride down the hill."

Down We Go

"Look, Father," said Mother.
"Sally is in the wagon.
Tuffy is in the wagon.
Ted is in the wagon, too."

"Down we go," said Ted.
"Down we go to Father.
Down we go to Mother.
Down the hill we go."

"Oh, Ted!" said Sally.
"Boots wants to ride, too.
He wants to ride in the wagon."

"No, Boots, no!" said Ted.
"Run down the hill, Boots.
Run, Boots, run!"

"Look, Father!" said Ted.
"Look, Mother.
Here we come.
Here we come down the hill!"

Down the hill went the wagon.
Down the hill went Ted.
Down the hill went Sally.
Down the hill went Tuffy, too.

The Play House

A House To Play In

Ted and Sally have a house.
It is a little house.
It is a house to play in.

"We have a house," said Sally.
"I like the little house.
I like to play in it."

"We have a house," said Ted.
"Sally can play in it.
I can play in it, too.
I like the play house."

"Oh, Ted!" said Sally.
"Tuffy likes the play house.
Look at Tuffy!"

"Here comes Boots," said Ted.
"He likes the play house, too."

Sally and Ted

"Ted," said Sally.
"I want to play house.
I will be the mother.
You can be the father.
Will you play house, Ted?
Will you be the father?"

"No, Sally," said Ted.
"I have my wagon.
I want to play with my wagon.
You can play house.
I am too big.
I am too big to play house."

"Ted!" said Sally.
"You are not too big.
You can play house.
You can be the father, Ted.
Come and play house."

"No, Sally, no!" said Ted.
"I am too big.
I am too big to play house."

Sally and Boots

"Here, Boots!" said Ted.
"You play with Sally.
You can play house.
You can be a big boy.
You can be a big, big boy."

"Oh, Boots!" said Sally.
"You can be my big boy.
We will play house.
You will like to play house.
You will like to be my boy."

"Look, Ted!" said Sally.
"See Boots run away.
He will not be my big boy."

"Sally," said Ted.
"Boots will not play house.
He will run away.
Go and get Tuffy.
Get Tuffy to play house."

Sally and Tuffy

"Tuffy," said Sally.
"We can play house.
I am the mother.
You are my little boy.
You will not run away.
Will you, Tuffy?"

"Oh! Oh! Oh!" said Sally.
"Look at Tuffy run away.
He will not be my little boy.
He will not play house."

Tuffy ran away.
He ran and ran and ran.

Boots ran away.

He did not want to be a boy.

He did not want to play house.

Tuffy ran away.

He did not want to be a boy.

He did not want to play house.

"Oh! Oh! Oh!" said Sally.

The Dolls

"Mother," said Sally.
"My dolls will play house.
Here is my boy doll.
He will play house.
He will not run away."

"No, Sally," said Mother.
"He will not run away."

"Look, Mother," said Sally.
"Here is my girl doll, too.
I will play with my girl doll.
I will play with my boy doll.
Oh, I like my dolls."

"Go and play," said Mother.
"Play in the play house, Sally."

Sally ran to the play house.

The dolls did not run away.

"Oh!" said Sally.
"The dolls like to play.
Here is my little boy.
Here is my little girl.
I am the mother.
We will play house."

Girls Play House

"Look, Sally," said Ted.
"Here come two girls.
They have dolls.
They have come to play."

"Come in, girls," said Sally.
"Come in and play."

42

"Look, Sally," said the girls.
"We have dolls.
Here is one big doll.
Here are two little dolls."

"Oh! Oh!" said Sally.
"One doll is big.
It is a big, big doll.
Two dolls are little.
They are little, little dolls.
Here are my dolls, too."

43

Sally and the girls played.
They played house.

"Oh, Sally!" said the girls.
"We like to play with you.
We like to play house."

They played and played.

44

Boys Play Train

"Look, Ted," said Sally.
"Here come two boys."

"Here we are," said the boys.
"We have two wagons.
We have come to play.
We want to play train."

"Look, boys!" said Ted.
"Here is my wagon, too.
We have three wagons.
They can be three cars.
We can have a big train."

"One, two, three," said a boy.
"We will have a big train.
We will have three cars in it."

Away went the three boys.
Away went the three cars.
Away went the big train.

"Choo-choo!" said Ted.
"Choo-choo! Choo-choo!
Look at the big train!
Choo-choo! Choo-choo!"

Ride in the Big Train

"Here, Boots!" a boy said.
"You can ride in the train.
You can ride in my car."

Boots ran to the train.
"Jump in, Boots," the boy said.
"Jump in and ride.
Look, Ted.
Boots likes to ride."

"Here, Tuffy!" a boy said.
"You can ride, too.
You can ride in my car."

Tuffy ran away.
He did not want to ride.

"Look at Tuffy!" said Ted.
"He will not ride in the train.
Boots will ride.
Here we go.
Choo-choo!   Choo-choo!"

The boys played with the train.
They went up the hill.
Up they went with the train.

"Choo-choo!" said the boys.
"Here comes the big train.
One car, two cars, three cars!
Up the hill we go."

"Choo-choo!" said the boys.
"Here we go down the hill.
Here comes the big train.
Choo-choo! Choo-choo!"

Down the hill went the train.
Down went the three boys.
Down the hill went Boots, too.
Choo-choo! Choo-choo!

The Dolls Ride

"Look, girls," said Ted.
"See the big train.
Do you want to ride?"

"Yes, yes," said Sally.
"We want to ride."

"Yes, yes," said the two girls.
"We do want to ride."

"Come here, Boots," said Ted.
"The girls want to ride.
The dolls want to ride, too."

"Get in," said the boys.
"Get in the cars.
Get in the big train."

"One, two, three!" said Ted.
"Here we go.
Choo-choo!   Choo-choo!"

Away went the big train.
Choo-choo! Choo-choo!

Away went Sally.
Away went the two girls.
Away went the dolls.

"Choo-choo!" said the girls.
"Choo-choo! Choo-choo!
Here comes the train!"

Here We Go
to the Farm

Come to the Farm

Ted and Sally have a grandmother.
Ted and Sally have a grandfather.

Grandmother is at the farm.
Grandfather is at the farm.

"I want to see Ted,"
said Grandmother.
"I want to see Sally."

"Yes," said Grandfather.
"I want to see Ted.
I want to see Sally, too.
We will have Ted and Sally
come to the farm."

"Ted and Sally,"
said Grandmother.

"We want to see you.
Come to the farm.
Get Mother to come with you.
Do come to the farm."

"They will come,"
said Grandfather.

"They will come to the farm."

"Ted and Sally," said Mother.
"Grandmother wants you
to come to the farm.
Do you want to go?
We will see Grandmother.
We will see Grandfather."

"Oh, yes!" said Ted and Sally.
"We want to see Grandmother.
We want to see Grandfather.
We want to go to the farm."

Boots and Tuffy

"Boots," said Ted.
"We are going to the farm.
Mother is going.
Sally is going.
Do you want to go
to the farm?"

"Oh, yes!" said Sally.
"Boots wants to go."

"Tuffy," said Sally.
"We are going to the farm.
I want you to go, too.
Do you want to go, Tuffy?"

"Oh, yes!" said Ted.
"Tuffy wants to go.
Boots is going.
Tuffy wants to go with Boots."

"Ted! Ted!" said Sally.
"We will ride on the train
to the farm."

"Yes, Sally!" said Ted.
"We will ride on the train.
Choo-choo! Choo-choo!
Boots is going to ride
on the train.
Tuffy is going to ride
on the train.
Choo-choo! Choo-choo!"

Here We Go

"Come," said Father.
"We will go to the train."

"Oh, Father!" said Sally.
"I want you to go
to the farm, too."

"Sally," said Father.
"I can not go with you.
But I will come to the farm."

"Come, Sally," said Mother.
"Father can not go.
But it will be fun
to see Grandmother.
It will be fun
to see Grandfather."

"Yes, Sally," said Father.
"You will have fun
on the train, too."

Away they went to the train.

The Big Train

"Look, Boots!" said Ted.
"Look at the big train!
You are going to ride on it.
Tuffy is going to ride
on the big train, too.
It will be fun."

"Come, Boots," said Ted.
"You will ride in this car.
Tuffy will ride with you.
Sally and I can not ride
in this car.

But we will be on the train.
Jump in the car, Boots."

"Ted," said Father.
"Here is the man."

Ted said to the man,
"This is my dog.
This is Boots.
He is going to ride with you."

"Here, Boots!" said the man.
"I like dogs."

Boots went to the man.

Sally said to the man,
"This is my cat.
This is Tuffy.
He is going to ride
in the car with you.
But I will be on the train."

"My!" said the man.
"He is a big cat.
I like cats.
I like to have dogs and cats
ride in my car."

"Good-by, Tuffy," said Sally.
"We will be on the train."

"Good-by, Boots," said Ted.
"We can not ride in this car.
But we will be on the train.
Good-by, Boots."

"Good-by," said Father.
"Good-by, Ted and Sally.
Good-by, Mother.
Have fun on the farm."

"Good-by," said Ted and Sally.
"Good-by, Father.
Here we go on the big train."

On the Train

"Oh, Mother!" said Sally.
"I like this train."

"I like it, too," said Ted.
"I like to ride on the train."

"Ted and Sally," said Mother.
"You can play on the train."

"Oh, yes!" said Sally.
"I can play with my doll."

"Look, Mother," said Ted.
"Look at my little boat.
I can play with it."

Ted and Sally played.
On and on went the train.

We Eat on the Train

"Come, Sally," said Mother.
"We will get something to eat."

"This will be fun," said Sally.
"I want to eat on the train."

"Yes," said Ted.
"I want something to eat."

"Ted and Sally," said Mother.
"Do you like this car?"

"Oh, yes!" said Ted and Sally.
"This is fun!"

"Look," said Mother.
"We will have something
good to eat."

They did have something
good to eat.

"Mother," said Ted.

"We want something good
for Boots to eat.

We want something for Tuffy."

Ted said to the man,

"We have a dog and a cat
on the train.

They want something to eat."

"I will get something,"
said the man.

"Thank you," said Mother.

"Thank you," said Ted.
"Boots will like this."

"Thank you," said Sally.
"This will be good for Tuffy.
Tuffy will like this."

"Come," said Mother.
"We will go
and see Tuffy and Boots."

"Good-by,"
said Ted to the man.
"Good-by," said Sally.

"Look, Boots!" said Ted.
"Here is something to eat."

"Look, Tuffy!" said Sally.
"Here is something for you."

"Boots is a good dog,"
said the man.
"And Tuffy is a good cat."

"Oh, thank you!"
said Ted and Sally.

To Bed on the Train

"Ted and Sally," said Mother.
"I want you to go to bed."

"Yes, Mother," said Ted.

"Oh, Ted!" said Sally.
"We are going to bed
on the train!"

"This is fun!" said Ted.

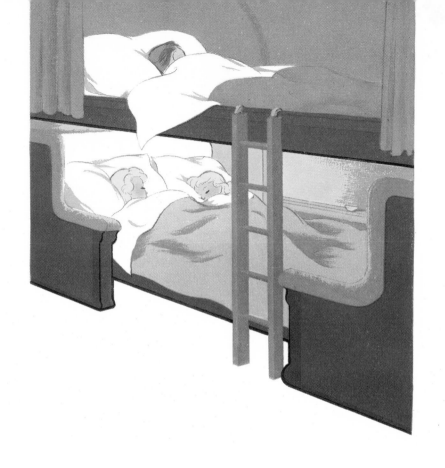

Ted went to bed.
Sally went to bed.
Mother went to bed.
They went to bed on the train.

On and on went the train.

"Get up, Ted," said Mother.
"Sally and I are up."

"Oh, Ted!" said Sally.
"We are going to see
Grandfather and Grandmother.
Get up, Ted, get up!"

"Here I come," said Ted.

Grandfather

"Mother," said Sally.
"I see Grandfather."

"Oh, Grandfather!" said Ted.
"Here we are!"

"My, my!" said Grandfather.
"How big you are, Ted!
You are a big boy."

Sally ran to Grandfather.

"My, my!" said Grandfather.
"How big you are, Sally!
You are a big girl.
Come, Mother.
My car is here.
We will ride to the farm.
Grandmother is at the farm."

"Grandfather," said Ted.
"We have a dog and a cat.
They are on the train."

"Oh, yes!" said Sally.
"We have to get
Boots and Tuffy."

Grandfather laughed.
"Boots and Tuffy!" he said.
"I will go with you
to get Boots and Tuffy."

"Here they are," said the man.
"Boots is a good dog.
And Tuffy is a good cat."

"Thank you," said Sally.

"My, my!" said Grandfather.
"How are you, Boots?
How are you, Tuffy?"

The man laughed.
Ted and Sally laughed.
Grandfather laughed.

Grandmother

"This is my car,"
said Grandfather.
"Get in, Mother.
Get in, Ted and Sally."

"Get in, Boots," said Ted.

Away they went to the farm.

"Look," said Mother.
"Here is the farm."

"Oh, oh!" said Sally.
"Here is the big yellow house."

"And Grandmother!" said Ted.
"Here is Grandmother!"

"My, oh, my!" said Grandmother.
"How big you are, Ted!
How big you are, Sally!
My! It is good to see you!"

Blue Hill Farm

Farm Boy and Farm Girl

"Ted," said Grandfather.
"You look like a farm boy now.
And look at Sally!
She looks like a farm girl."

"She can play now," said Ted.
"I can play now, too.
We can have fun
on Blue Hill Farm."

"Come on, Ted," said Sally.
"I want to see the chickens.
I want to see the big hens."

"Yes, Sally," said Ted.
"We will go with Grandfather.
We will look at the hens
and the chickens.
   Come here, Boots, come here!"

"Come, Tuffy," said Sally.
"We are going
to see the chickens now."

Tuffy and the Red Hen

"Sally," said Ted.
"Look at the big hen.
She is a big red hen."

"Yes, Ted," said Sally.
"Tuffy sees the red hen, too.
Tuffy wants to play
with the big red hen."

Tuffy ran to the red hen.
But the red hen did not want
to play with Tuffy.

"Cluck! Cluck!" said the hen.
"Cluck! Cluck! Cluck!
Go away, cat, go away!"

"Oh, Tuffy!" said Ted.
"Hens do not play with cats."

The big red hen ran at Tuffy.
"Cluck! Cluck!" she said.

Tuffy ran to Sally.
He did not want to play now.
He did not like the red hen.

Boots and the Ducks

"Look, Sally!" said Ted.
"Look at the ducks!"

"Oh, yes!" said Sally.
"I see the mother duck.
I see the little yellow ducks.
Look at the ducks splash!
Splash, yellow ducks, splash!"

Sally laughed and laughed.

Boots wanted to splash, too.
In he went.
Splash! Splash! Splash!

Boots wanted to play
with the yellow ducks.
But the mother duck
did not like Boots.
"Quack! Quack!" she said.
"Go away, dog, go away!"

"Quack! Quack!" said the duck.
"Get out, dog, get out!
You can not get my little ducks.
Quack! Quack! Quack! Quack!"

"Come out, Boots!" said Ted.

Splash! Splash! Splash!
Boots ran out.

Sally laughed and laughed.
"You are funny ducks," she said.
"Funny, funny yellow ducks!"

94

The Blue Boat

"Oh Sally!" said Ted.
"See the blue boat."

"Grandfather," said Sally.
"We want to ride in the boat."

"Come," said Grandfather.
"We will go for a ride."

"Grandfather," said Ted.
"Sally and I
will make the boat go."

"Oh, yes, Grandfather!"
said Sally.
"We can make the boat go."

Ted and Sally wanted
to make the boat go.
But it did not go.

How Ted and Sally did splash!
But the blue boat did not go.

96

"Look, Ted and Sally,"
said Grandfather.
"Now! One! Two! Three!"

Away went the blue boat.
"We did make it go," said Ted.

"Good!" said Grandfather.
"One! Two! Three!
One! Two! Three!"

Boots was in the blue boat.
He looked at the mother duck.
She looked at Boots.

"Quack! Quack!" she said.
"Go away, dog, go away!
Quack! Quack! Quack!"

Boots did not have to go away.
Boots was in the boat now.

Grandfather laughed.
"This is funny," he said.

The Pet Pig

"Ted," said Grandmother.
"You have a dog for a pet.
I have a pet pig.
Here is my pet pig."

Ted looked at the pet pig.
"My!" said Ted.
"How big he is!"

"Yes," said Grandmother.
"He was a little pet pig.
But he is a big pet pig now."

"Oh, Grandmother!" said Ted.
"He is a funny big pig.
I like the pet pig.
I want the pet pig to like me."

"Look, Ted," said Grandmother.
"Do this for the pet pig.
He will like you."

"He likes me," said Ted.
"The pet pig likes me now."

Find the Eggs

"Ted and Sally,"
said Grandmother.

"Will you find the eggs
for me?"

"Oh, yes!" said Ted and Sally.
"It will be fun.
We will find the eggs."

They looked for the eggs.
It was fun.

"Look, Ted," said Sally.
"See the big red hen.
We will find eggs there."

"Yes," said Ted.
"We will get the eggs."

"There they are, Ted,"
said Sally.
"One, two, three eggs!"

Pig! Pig! Pig!

"Come on, Sally," said Ted.
"A hen went in there.
We can find eggs in there."

"No, no, Ted!" said Sally.
"Do not go in there.
The pet pig went in there."

But Ted went in.
He wanted to find the eggs.

Sally looked for Grandfather.
There he was.

"Oh, Grandfather!" said Sally.
"Come and get Ted."

But Grandfather said,
"I have something for the pigs.
Come with me.
You can see the pigs eat."

"Pig! Pig!" said Grandfather.
"Come, pig! Come, pig!"

How the pigs did come!
And the pet pig came, too.

"Oh, Grandfather!" said Sally.
"Look at Ted!"

Out came the pet pig.
And out came Ted.
He was on the pet pig.

The pet pig ran.
He wanted something to eat.

Down went Ted!

Grandfather laughed.
He laughed and laughed.

How Sally laughed!
"Oh, Ted!" she said.
"You looked funny
on the pet pig."

"Ted," said Sally.
"Did you find the hen?
Did you find the eggs?"

Ted laughed.
"No, Sally," he said.
"I did not find the hen.
I did not find the eggs.
But I did find the pet pig!"

We Ride the Horses

"Ted and Sally,"
said Grandfather.
"Do you like
to ride the horses?"

"Oh, yes!" said Ted.
"I like to ride
the big red horse."

"I like this horse,"
said Sally.
"He is a little horse.
I can ride this horse."

"Grandfather," said Ted
"It was fun
to go for the cows.
We like to ride the horses
and get the cows."

"Oh, yes!" said Sally.
"Look at the big cows.
One, two, three big cows!
I like the cows."

"Look at Boots," said Ted.
"This was fun for Boots, too.
He likes to go for the cows."

"There is Grandmother,"
said Grandfather.
"We will have
something good to eat now."

"I like the farm," said Ted.
"It was fun to ride the horses.
It was fun to go
for the cows."

"I like the farm, too,"
said Sally.
"I like the hens and chickens.
I like the yellow ducks.
The ducks are funny."

"Yes," said Ted.
"The pet pig is funny, too."

Sally laughed at Ted.
She laughed and laughed.

111

Father Is Coming

"Ted and Sally," said Mother.
"Father is coming
to Blue Hill Farm."

"Yes," said Grandmother.
"He is coming on the train."

"Oh, oh!" said Ted and Sally.
"Father is coming!
Father is coming to the farm."

"I see the train," said Ted.
"The train is coming."

"Oh, yes!" said Sally.
"There it is, Mother.
There is the train.
Father is on the train."

"Come, Grandmother,"
said Grandfather.
"The train is coming."

Father was on the train.
There he was.

"My!" said Grandmother.
"It is good to see you!"

"Ted and Sally," said Father.
"How do you like the farm?"

"Oh, we like it!"
said Ted and Sally.

"Come," said Grandfather.
"We will go to the farm."

The Farm Is Fun

"Father," said Ted.
"I want you to see the farm.
We can ride in the blue boat.
We can find the eggs.
We can go for the cows."

"Yes, Ted," said Father.
"I will go with you.
I want to see all the farm."

Away went Ted and Father
to see the big farm.

115

"Look at Grandfather!"
said Ted.

Ted and Father looked
at Grandfather.
On and on Grandfather went.

Father went with Ted
to see the hens.
They looked
at the little yellow chickens.

They looked at all the pigs.
"Look, Father!" said Ted.
"See this big pig!
He is a pet pig."

They looked
at the mother duck.
They looked
at all the funny little ducks.

They looked at the cows.
Ted wanted Father to see
all the farm.

"Oh! Oh!" said Ted.
"There is Grandmother.
Now we will all have
something good to eat.
Run, Father, run!"

Ted ran to the house.
Father ran to the house.

Grandmother laughed.
"They want something to eat,"
she said.

How they did eat!

Ted and Sally,
Mother and Father,
Grandmother and Grandfather!

How they all did eat!

Going Home

"Ted and Sally," said Mother.
"The farm is fun.
But we have to go home."

"Yes, Mother," said Ted.
"We have to go home."

"Oh, Grandmother!" said Sally.
"The farm was fun!
But we have to go home now."

"Sally," said Grandmother.
"It was fun to have you here.
You are a good girl, Sally.
And Ted is a good boy."

Ted and Sally said "Good-by"
to the farm.

They said "Good-by"
to the horses and the cows.

They said "Good-by"
to the hens and the chickens.

They said "Good-by"
to the little yellow ducks.

They said "Good-by"
to the pet pig.

"Good-by, Blue Hill Farm,"
said Ted and Sally.

"We have to go home now."

They all went to the train.

"Good-by, Grandmother,"
said Ted and Sally.
"Good-by, Grandfather.
The farm was fun.
Thank you! Thank you!"

"Good-by, Ted and Sally,"
said Grandmother.

"Good-by, Ted and Sally,"
said Grandfather.

"Oh, Father!" said Ted.
"How I did like the farm!"

"I did, too," said Sally.
"I did like Blue Hill Farm.
But I like this train, too."

"Father," said Ted.
"Make up a story.
Make up a farm story."

"Yes, Father!" said Sally.
"Have a farm in the story.
Have a train in the story, too."

Father laughed.
"You have to go to bed,"
he said.

Father looked at Mother.
Mother laughed.
"Make up a story," she said.
"Make up a funny story
for Ted and Sally."

Here is the story.

Funny Big Farm
and
Funny Little Train

On the Funny Farm

Mr. Horse and Mr. Pig
have a farm.
It is a big farm.

Mr. Horse and Mr. Pig
have a house on the farm.

"It is a good house,"
said Mr. Horse.

There is a house
for Mrs. Duck on the farm.
She likes the house.
All the little ducks
like the house, too.

The little yellow ducks
splash and play.
They have fun.

There is a house
for Mrs. Hen on the farm.
She likes the house.
All the little chickens
like the house, too.

There is a house
for Mrs. Cow on the farm.
She likes the house.
She likes the big farm, too.

What Is It?

"Oh! Oh! Oh!" said Mr. Pig.
"Something is coming.
What is it?"

"My! My!" said Mr. Horse.
"What is it?"

"Look! Look!" said Mrs. Cow.
"What is it?"

129

"Quack! Quack!" said Mrs. Duck.
"Something is coming.
What is it?"

"Cluck! Cluck!" said Mrs. Hen.
"Run, little chickens, run!"

130

"Now! Now!" said Mr. Pig.
"Do not run away.
I see what it is.
It can not get you.
It is a train."

"A train!" said Mrs. Hen.

"A train!" said Mrs. Duck.
"A train on the farm?"

It was a train.
It was a little red train.

"Choo-choo!" said the train.
"I like this farm."

The Little Red Train

"Mr. Pig," said Mr. Horse.
"We can not have a train
on this farm.
I will make the train
go away."

Mr. Horse went to the train.
"Now, see here!" he said.
"This is my farm.
You can not come
on this farm.
Mr. Pig and I do not want
a train on this farm."

"But I like this farm,"
said the little red train.

"We do not like you,"
said Mr. Horse.
"Go away! Go away!"

Mr. Pig came.
"Go away, train, go away!"
he said.

The little red train laughed.
"Oh, Mr. Pig!" he said.
"Come and ride on me.
You will like to ride.
Get Mrs. Hen and Mrs. Duck.
Get the little yellow ducks
and the little chickens.
You can all have a ride."

Mr. Pig looked at Mr. Horse.
"I do want to ride
on a train," said Mr. Pig.

Mr. Horse laughed.
"Go on and ride," he said.

A Funny Ride

"I will get Mrs. Duck,"
said Mr. Pig.

"I will get Mrs. Hen.

I will get the little ducks
and the little chickens.

We can all ride
on the train."

"I will get Mrs. Cow,"
said Mr. Horse.

"She and I will see you
ride on the train."

Mrs. Duck came
with all the little ducks.

Mrs. Hen came
with all the little chickens.

"Get on," said the train.
"Get on, Mrs. Duck.
Get on, Mrs. Hen.
Get on, Mr. Pig.
Get on and ride.
Choo-choo!"

Away they went.

"Oh, this is fun!" they said.

"This is fun! This is fun!"

"Choo-choo! Choo-choo!"
said the little red train.

138

"Look, Mr. Horse!"
said Mrs. Cow.
"Here they come!"

"My! My!" said Mr. Horse.
"Look at the train
come down the big hill!"

Mr. Horse and Mrs. Cow
laughed and laughed.

"I have to go now,"
said the little red train.
   "Did you like the ride?"

   "Oh, yes!" they all said.
"We thank you for the ride."

   "We all thank you,"
said Mr. Horse.
   "We thank you for coming
to the farm."

"Now," said the little train.
"I have to go home.
Good-by! Good-by!"

"Good-by, little train,"
said Mr. Horse.

"Good-by, little train,"
they all said.
"Good-by! Good-by!"

Away the little train went.
"Choo-choo! Good-by!"
he said.

To be read to children

Rainy Day at the Farm

The chickens run inside the coop
  As fast as they can get
As soon as it begins to rain,
  They do not like the wet.

The horses droop their heads and tails
  And sulk about the rain.
The cows all gather in the barn
  And won't go out again.

The kittens sit with ruffled fur.
  The turkeys make a fuss.
But all the ducks are full of joy
  And come to play with us!

   Grateful acknowledgment is made to Marchette Chute and to
The Macmillan Company for the use of the poem, "Rainy Day
at the Farm," from *Rhymes about the Country*, by Marchette
Chute, copyright, 1941, by The Macmillan Company.

Word List

The following list contains all the new words — 81 in number — that occur in *Ted and Sally*, basal primer of *The Macmillan Readers*. The 40 words introduced in *Splash* and *Tuffy and Boots*, basal pre-primers, are repeated, making a total primer vocabulary of 121 words. With the exception of sound words and the names of characters, they are words frequently found in children's reading.

1.	24.	46. three	67. man
2.	25. house	cars	dog
3.	26. a	47. choo-choo	68. cat
4.	have	48.	69. good-by
5. wagon	27.	49.	70.
6.	28. can	50.	71.
7.	29.	51.	72.
8.	30. be	52. do	73. eat
9.	31. am	yes	something
10.	32. not	53.	74. good
11.	33. boy	54.	75. for
12.	34.	55. farm	thank
13.	35. away	56. grandmother	76.
14. no	36.	grandfather	77.
15.	37. ran	57.	78. bed
16. are	38. did	58.	79.
too	39. dolls	59.	80.
17.	40. girl	60. going	81. how
18. hill	41.	61.	82.
19.	42. two	62. on	83. laughed
20. went	they	63. but	84.
21.	43. one	64. fun	85.
22.	44. played	65.	86. yellow
23.	45. train	66. this	87. blue

88. now
she
89. chickens
hens
90. red
91. cluck
92. ducks
93. wanted
quack
94. out
funny
95.
96. make
97.
98. was
looked
99. pet
pig
100. me
101. find
eggs
102. there
103.
104.
105. came
106.
107.
108. horses
109. cows
110.
111.
112. coming
113.
114.
115. all
116.
117.
118.
119.
120. home
121.
122.
123. story
124.
125.
126. Mr.
127. Mrs.
128.
129. what
130.
131.
132.
133.
134.
135.
136.
137.
138.
139.
140.
141.
142.